Jonah and the Whale

Miles Kelly

One day God spoke to a man named Jonah. "Go to the city of Nineveh. Tell the people there to change their **wicked ways.**"

NINEVEH

Jonah didn't want to do this. So he set off, going the opposite way.

Jonah found a ship that was travelling far away. The captain kindly let him on board.

As soon as the ship was on its way,
God sent a **terrible** storm.

Rain lashed down, lightning flashed and great waves threw the ship back and forth.

"It's my fault!" Jonah cried.
"You'll have to throw me overboard."
He told the sailors that he was
running away from God.

The sailors had no choice – they **threw** Jonah into the waves. The storm quickly came to an end.

Jonah sank
through the deep,
dark waters.

Suddenly a huge whale loomed from the darkness, sent by God. The whale opened its great mouth and swallowed Jonah whole.

For three days, Jonah was stuck in the smelly gloom of the **whale's stomach**. He was very sorry and prayed to God for forgiveness.

God knew Jonah had learned his lesson. The whale finally **spat him out** onto a sandy shore.

"Now go to Nineveh and deliver my message," God told Jonah. "If the people don't behave better I will destroy the city in forty days."

This time Jonah did
as he was told and
travelled to Nineveh.

Marching through the city, Jonah called out, "God will **destroy** the city in forty days unless you change your wicked ways!"

Word soon spread and
the people were scared.

Jonah also told the king of Nineveh. He was shocked, and ordered the people to mend their ways at once.

The people were sorry and decided to be good from then on.

They prayed to God and were kind and helpful to each other. God forgave them.

After forty days, Jonah went into the desert and waited.

Nothing happened – Nineveh was spared. "You should have punished those bad people!" Jonah cried angrily.

God decided to teach Jonah a lesson. He made a plant shoot up, to shade him from the hot desert sun.

The next day, God sent insects to eat the plant so it died. This upset Jonah.

"If you're sad about a plant," God told him, "how do you think I would have felt if all the people and animals of Nineveh had been lost?"

At last, Jonah understood that God had enough love for all living things.